HIGH FIVE THIS SIGN

How to Use This Book

These street flyers are designed to make your neighborhood and nearby surroundings just a little more magical. Simply tear out each flyer, and tape to a street pole to instantly deliver a tiny moment of joy to the world around you. For best results, place each flyer in a high visibility area to assure maximum joy for the most amount of people.

Obvious Plant street flyers are a small part of a larger project created by Jeff Wysaski. Through the use of flyers, store signage and other media, the ultimate goal is to break up the monotony of everyday life by 'planting' humor in unsuspecting places.

For more Obvious Plant check
obviousplant.com
twitter.com/obviousplant_
fb.com/obviousplant
instagram.com/obviousplant

D1408813

ISBN: 978-0-9977194-1-3

10 9 8 7 6 5 4 3 2 1

Printed in China

© 2016 Jeff Wysaski

by Jeff Wysaski

WANTED

★ DEAD OR ALIVE ★

The Squirrel that stole my bagel!

I turned around for one second and he just took it right off my plate.

Reward: I will buy you a bagel.

For sale:
Legendary Sword

Keeps trying to lead
me on a noble journey
of heroism, and quite
frankly, I'd rather just
stay in bed and do nothing.

*For more info, please
email swordguy626@gmail.com*

WANTED

People to come watch me do sick judo moves in the park

LIGHTNING KICKS!

BOARD BREAKS!

This Saturday
11 am to 12:30 pm

WALL RUNNING!

LEG SWEEPS!

No $$$ but trust me
YOU WILL BE PAID
IN INSPIRATION

WHO IS A GOOD BOY?

Is it me?

me

Please tell me, I need to know.

You are a good boy   No. Bad dog!   You are a good boy   No. Bad dog!   You are a good boy   No. Bad dog!   You are a good boy   No. Bad dog!   You are a good boy   No. Bad dog!   You are a good boy   No. Bad dog!   You are a good boy   No. Bad dog!

Good things come to...

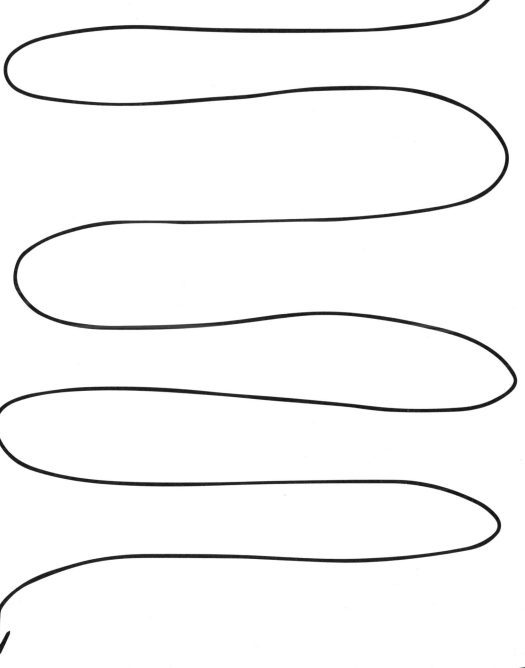

...those who wait. See, there's a panda at the end of this flyer.

What kind of train eats too much?

A CHEW CHEW TRAIN
AhAHAHAHaha HAHAhahaHAH AHAhah...

**omg please call me
I'm so lonely
I need friends...
206-651-4237**

HIGH FIVE THIS HAND!

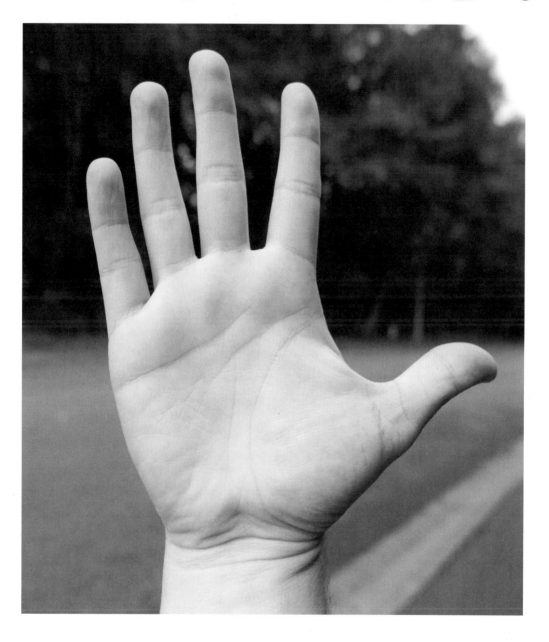

Please? I live a very sad life.
This is all I have.

I.T. Jobs Available!

Do you want a job in I.T.?

Experienced Iguana Translators needed to relay my orders to the army of trained lizards in my basement. For more info, please call:

385-355-4492
(ask for Lizard King)

No pay, but once my reign of terror begins I PROMISE I SHALL KILL YOU LAST

⊙ Stop walking! ⊙

Keith has challenged you to a staring contest!

Keith

Do not ignore his challenge!

ONLY A COWARD WOULD JUST KEEP WALKING.

DO NOT READ THIS SIGN!

Hey! What did I just tell you?
Seriously, STOP READING.

JUST. STOP.

Keep walking.

Go away...

Okay, good I think they're gon-

OH MY GOD
YOU'RE STILL HERE?

What part of 'DO NOT READ'
do you not understand!?

I DREW THIS PICTURE OF A DRAGON

PLEASE CHOOSE A COMPLIMENT

Good job

So realistic

Nice flames

Are you Picasso?

You sure that's not an actual dragon?

Two thumbs up!

I'm scared

Way to go!

Can I tattoo this on my arm?

High five!

This should be in a museum

I love you

WHOA!

This made my day

Free robot legs!

Upgrade your own body or use them to build a robot army. Your choice.

WANTED

New son who isn't a big giant dork

Auditions this Sunday in park

Things to bring:
1. List of fave pro wrestlers
2. Funyuns
3. Cool ninja swords if you have them

Please pet this picture of a dog! He is a loyal pup and needs your love.

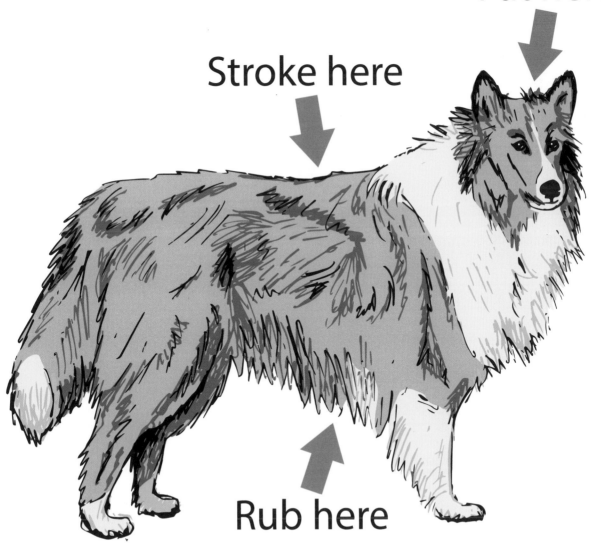

Pat here

Stroke here

Rub here

Caw!

Caw Caw Caw Caw.
Caw CAW Caw.

 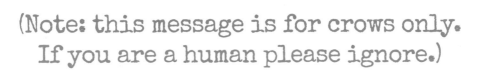

(Note: this message is for crows only.
If you are a human please ignore.)

I am trying to give every street pole a name because all street poles should have names.

Should this one be Steven or Craigbert?

Steven   **Craigbert**

For results and to see the names of other street poles, visit NameThisStreetPole.com

Help!

A lightning bolt struck this street pole as I was putting up this flyer and now I'm trapped inside the paper! Please help me escape or at least tell my mom I am alive (but very scared).

I'm a morning person and an afternoon slime monster PLEASE HELP this gremlin's curse is killing my social life

If you know how to destroy dark magic, please meet me here tomorrow at 10:30 a.m.

Buried treasure

PLEASE DO NOT DIG IT UP!
This is just a reminder to myself.

MISSED CONNECTION

**You were the girl sitting on this park bench,
I was the guy fighting a duck for my pants
and losing**

**If you saw me,
please call me
614-344-8994**

(p.s. I got them back - let's hang out!)

- Found Dog -

- Male.
- Not sure of breed but it is
white with black spots.
- Big ears.
- Fluffy tail.
- Is 8-feet tall.
- Has forked lizard tongue.
- Eyes glow red when it is angry.
- Ate my neighbor.
- FOUND NEAR POWER PLANT.

Please come get if it is yours

DO NOT REMOVE *THIS FLYER*

I have trapped a warlock behind it and if you remove it his dark magic will destroy us all!